MW00777242

Cyberwit.net
HIG 45 Kaushambi Kunj, Kalindipuram
Allahabad - 211011 (U.P.) India
http://www.cyberwit.net
Tel: +(91) 9415091004 +(91) (532) 2552257
E-mail: info@cyberwit.net

Printed at Repro India Limited.

Slumber Party Suicide Pact

[Stories]

Matthew Dexter

For México, whatever that is. And dedicated to all my
enemies—I will destroy you.

Dear Reader

I am trying to pry open your casket
with this burning snowflake.

—James Tate, "Dear Reader"

Then it is dark; it is a night where kings in golden suits ride elephants over the mountains.

—John Cheever, "A Country Husband"

Zamboni

We're snorting fluorescent goo from fireflies on the roof

of the rink. I'd been driving the Zamboni since midnight.

The ice is fresh and glowing. I blow blistered fingers.

Fog obscures the blue line. A yellow school bus careens

toward the parking lot on a patch of black ice. White

kids with hockey bags and sticks marching with the

energy of fire ants. Fathers juggling Styrofoam cups,

mothers' camouflaged muffin tops beneath mink coats.

Camel smoke swirls from mittens. Lipstick glimmers on

Marlboro butts in the slush in front of the entrance.

These people are animals.

We don't play hockey. They call us niggers behind

our backs. We can't fit our skates over our sneakers. Our

parents are zombie crackheads. The Zamboni is my

slave-ship. Our great-great-grandchildren are captains of

spaceships.

Ashley smuggles fireflies in her North Face.

Ashley's a white girl. She breeds them. Her Daddy brews

bathtub gin in his Homer Simpson boxer shorts. We'd

been smoking bed bugs all winter. Eyeballing vodka and

orange juice. Ashley shimmers, spun by cumulonimbus,

fingers inside, ladybugs behind bloodshot eyeballs.

Morons swagger from their locker rooms. I consider

somersaulting from the roof of the rink. A cannonball

into a mound of lipsticked butts.

They have filters: the hockey players. Never say

shit to our faces. We're the seeds of base-heads. Our

ancestors hung from trees. I can feel my pulse inside

Ashley. Yesterday's bunk. I got busted jacking

fluorescent butt plugs. They'll print my face in the local

newspaper tonight. Embarrassed by what the cashier

might think—I'll take it up the butt from the whole town.

I peel glow-in-the-dark condoms from my wallet

and burn rubbers in the Zamboni garage. Can't be identified by these expiration dates. Bubba's sharpening skates. You can hear sparks flying from the blades. Mothers with rabbit fur coats sucking hazelnut coffee through porcelain veneers. Ashley on her iPhone at the edge of the splintered bleachers. Parents screaming obscenities. Juvenile delinquents skating with purple veins. Men wrestling the obstinate scoreboard, lacing Starbucks cappuccinos with whiskey.

Racists dig me from the snowbank. Monsters never make love inside an igloo. They yank my hairy legs and make a wish. My vertebra is broken. The ice is glowing. My groin tears. I'm bleeding fluorescent snot into fresh snow.

The Mexican Conductor

Meth made the miniature train more endurable as it

careened through the mall. Children chased the caboose.

Eyes full of diamonds and watermelons and blood,

pointing with cotton candy dusted fingertips as the

majesty blasts its convivial horn. I think of *muchachos*

and *muchachas* who ride with their siblings or mothers

or babysitters. How they bounce. How they should be

lost in a cave with nothing but fire. How steel melts

beneath the broken wings of fallen serpents.

Canopy Bed

Every night I pick a juicy booger and wipe it onto the wallpaper behind my canopy bed. This is my thing. Like a prisoner counting days 'til release. I have been doing this my whole life. Layers of nasal offerings pasted onto ancient wallpaper. It is like those rings within trees and how you can count the years. Mom has no idea.

'Til they load my desk and dresser into the truck. The room is empty except for the canopy bed. I beg for another hour. Childhood coagulated beneath fingernails like glowing wings from fireflies. Scrape them against bubblegum pavements and swallow the obstinate fossils that refuse to dislodge. Chewed memories from bullies: cool girls with flat bellies, globs of jelly atop porcelain veneers, peanut butter on the roof of my mouth.

One of the movers wants to fuck me. Most men

do. I am fourteen. My boobs are small and beautiful. They must think my pussy is tight. I am naked and he smiles. The rest of the movers enter and everybody grunts. Mom left for a pack of Camels. Three humps. They take turns on top. One watches out my window. Muscles and shoulders scratched with mucus fingernails older than my mattress.

The headboard bashes boogers.

Mom returns. Asks why the bed is still here. The men are already in prison, counting the years. They saved me from removing the canopy. There would be time to carve the hardened snot and blood from the parts that matter most.

Officers offer to carry the bed onto the abandoned truck. They pull the canopy apart. Detectives see me doing cartwheels naked. They know that prison is an evil place so they can only look. They gawk at my

belly ring where boogers are glowing. Counting rings

within me.

Actual age: infinity.

They ogle 'til Mom screams and cradles me on

the mattress and asks what happened. We move the

headboard so she sees the treasure. We dig through the

years. She hugs me and blows camel smoke onto my

collage. She brushes the layered monument like an

archaeologist unearthing a dinosaur fossil. She sees me

naked again. Not just my skin but everything extinct.

Crabs Feasting on Eyeballs

When the dog died, I carried his corpse in my arms around the block 'til my running shoes were filled with blood and my toes loaded with blisters. The last time I saw my sister was after the argument that foreshadowed her catapult from the Golden Gate Bridge. I hear her bones cracking in my head as she hits the water. I feel the breeze and blood in her nose and imagine how the inertia took its toll. Men in white hazmat suits fishing for her corpse. She almost landed on a kite surfer.

When the pigeon passed away—after crashing through the kitchen window while we were washing dishes, I dug a hole in the backyard and we held a funeral—the whole family filling the grave with fertilizer. There are tombstones made of cardboard and Styrofoam with the dying dates scribbled in crayons by the children, nibbled by squirrels, often with a question mark in front of the hyphen because nobody knows for certain when an animal is born.

I can hear her crying as she somersaults from sunset into the Bay.

Strangers pry the running shoes from my blisters. New neighbors greet me in their front yard with my sister's dog displaying all its rigor mortis in furry fashion. The woman peels the sweaty tennis socks from my ankles. She smells like my sister after jogging. The children hide behind their father, away from the dog dangling from my shoulders. The veins on my forehead are throbbing through my headband.

My wife pulls up in the station wagon and the neighbors escort me inside. She fixes them lemonade and vodka as she pops the blisters with a freshly-sharpened golf pencil. He drinks yellow Arnold Palmer's with pulp; she prefers pink lemonade. I am hurting, certain these matters could wait 'til the dog was buried. My crotch itches. She should be sniffing their crotches as we speak. It kills me thinking about this.

Our souls are being trotted upon by giants. My blisters ooze into blue Kleenex. The dog is covered with a blanket so the children cannot see what a toll death takes. The barking from neighbors' yards is too much to handle, so throwing chicken and hamburgers on the grill is the only solution: losing myself in the black smoke exuding from charcoal briquettes smothered with lighter fluid. I caress the patties into heart shapes. My feet are bare; grass cushions the blisters.

Drowning in blood—imagine how it must feel. The puddles of pink bubbles collect on the blackening patties. The spatula sprinkles them into the charcoal like a wave washing upon the shore and plumes of sizzling smoke kiss the air.

The kite surfer heard her screaming. She lost her purse mid-plummet. He saw vitality and vigor in the cloudy Arctic of turquoise irises. Her splash submerged him.

I carry the dog from the front yard toward the grill. I do not disturb my cooking and while the kids are eating—when my wife is not looking—I carry the dog into the garage and close the door. It is not simple to amputate a family pet. Fleas and flaws and mosquitoes are bridging future with past, and I can see her in the bubbles as burgers burn and chicken catch fire.

It's Not Delivery, It's DiGiorno

I loitered behind the liquor store and exposed my severed

penis to tweens begging for beer. Before that I snorted

bath salts and flakka in front of a Domino's delivery

driver. Before that the pregnancy test confirmed what we

expected—life was backwards. Before that, under

duress, I signed divorce papers smeared with melted

mozzarella. Before that my wife threatened my scrotum

with rusty scissors meant for cutting slices of DiGiorno

Rising Crust Supreme Pizza. Before that Señor

Pepperoni snuggled flaccid inside crusty pajamas,

bourbon bulbous moonshine oozing into our bedroom,

an atavistic inertia of snores and subtle whimpers from

the bathroom where Nancy waved the pregnancy test

with the wisdom of a magic wand, eyeballs full of

fireflies and rheum. Before that we guzzled champagne

between shots of mescal in the bathtub. Before that we were in the shower making love after washing blood from faces, nipples, elbows, and armpits. Before that we juggled feces and giggled with glee. Before that the coroner left us alone. Before that we rode the magic carpet—cathartic fury flowing from broken capillaries. Before that a collage of feathers rained from a bloody eagle, beakless on shards of moonlit glass. Before that the chandelier trembled. Before that Nancy's mother scooped her last spoonful of mashed potatoes and swallowed a pistol, bullet devouring bald skull. Before that we were a family. Cancer spun her web, leukemia quivered from cobwebbed corners. Before that the kitchen filled with smoke, skinny gypsies dancing on broken toes. Before that we wheeled Nancy's mother into our lives. Before that we were ghosts.

Purple Heart

I stretch Grandpa's scrotum with the inertia of a butterfly
in a blender so the skin becomes translucent in the sun as
the nail gun spits its obstinate shadow. Blood oozes and
Grandpa's nuts and I was born to nail his sack to the
front porch. Dragonflies bounce, bloodshot eyeballs, the
taste of tears is the sound of singing shrapnel.

Too frail to fight back, geezer killed dozens of
Viet Cong before raping me. Maybe he fears the
memories will crumble into my skull like Zipperheads
ambushed by machine guns. His penis winking, sinking
into me, whiskey warm wet.

"Semper Fi," Grandpa says.

Nails are medieval. His unmown lawn is the
jungle and his moaning is conjuring curious neighbors
onto ramshackle porches. An old bearded woman points

her Budweiser bottle at us. I swagger down rotting steps,

slog through tall clammy grass, fire a few nails into

ballooning cumulonimbus. The sun vanishes.

"Please don't do this," Grandpa says.

Scrotum unfolding, each wrinkle a continent

expunged, an oyster map of the Atlantic, tornado

mocking me, Grandpa howls and I know the twister

hears because her funnel swoops down and zigzags

across the labyrinthine cornfield, catapulting cobs and

drizzling husks, melting street signs, wiping out porches,

flinging boards into faces—nails into eyeballs—

swallowing houses, shredding trees like toothpicks,

leaving toilets for tombstones and bathtubs where elderly

couples huddle in puddles of urine and collages of feces.

     We're lost and dancing in the dust of a butterfly's

wings. I wonder where the sound of weeping goes to die

and how her echo is eaten alive. My heartbeat is our

porch exploding, obliterating wingless cicadas and

decapitating dragonflies.

Crawlspace

My son has a secret drug closet—a crawlspace—nothing

but nails and insulation illuminated by black lights. I

crawl inside, squeezing crippled limbs through

diminutive door. My wheelchair's out of reach for the

first time. I feel like flying, getting high as Joshua does,

smoking trees with chums. A shark tooth necklace hangs

from the bulb. I yank it—crawling into his warm womb.

A glass bong glimmers in the corner beside an inflatable

crocodile. I knuckle the black light. The crawlspace is

packed with rubber women, humongous gaping mouths

and illimitable holes. I creep into the crocodile. I guzzle

bong water. My son was a normal kid before the

accident. My husband drove drunk across the median.

He's being sodomized in Beckley Correctional Center as

you read this. There's no doubt in my mind. I bleached

my anus the night before the accident. Now I can't even look at it in the mirror—my body doesn't jiggle like it used to. There are only so many angles a mirror can reflect. I gargle my son, resin of moonshine and dust. Angels chant from a baggie of mushrooms. This is his druggie lair. His friends come over and disappear, vanish with bud smoke. My daughter lost her virginity in this crawlspace with Granddaddy Purple in her lungs. I peel off my granny panties and light farts. Flatulence fills the crawlspace, fluorescent lighter: my magic carpet. Munching singed fur makes my skin crawl. I rope the noose around my neck. The rubber women stare. Stars fall from blackened ether—lost in his secret lair— termites gnawing hairy earlobes—Joshua holds me—our limbs unfurled. Insulation itching, the black light bounces into oblivion. Suffocation is a pearly wand.

This is my son's secret drug closet. When he came out to us the evening of the accident, my husband chugged a fifth of Smirnoff. I knew that rainbow-sherbet ice cream was the wisest method to stop Joshua from sobbing. We drove toward Baskin-Robbins as the moon hung orange over the freeway. I wiped my son's tears, and he held my hand in the backseat. I wrap the crocodile around my nipples. This is the way it was meant to be. I'm naked in this clandestine room borne from mourning. In the afternoon, Joshua will discover my ballooning body, my blue face glowing beneath the black light, my nipples hard, yellow incisors glowing whiter than approaching headlights.

Restraining Order

I am sitting in the attic closet with the cobwebs and mothballs, holding my baby, her hiccups ceaseless as the paint can smashes through the window below and the diaper rash is getting worse and cradling the freshly coated doorframe, they climb the pull-down ladder. They are dressed as clowns but they are my ex-wife's attorneys. They do their own dirty work. Do not care that nasal cavity cancer traps me in a cell every minute. I can smell them through the paint raising the dust with their humongous shoes. They reek of whisky, cigarettes, and bar pussy.

I am seeing shadows shaped like wrinkled and bloated imaginary friends who have not shown up in decades; pull me from the moment. What the hell happened to them? How did they get so damn old and ugly? One is too chubby to fit snugly between the shelves and the shoeboxes filled with baseball cards.

I stick my eyelashes into the wet slants. Her attorneys are young and strong, they feast off the papers and ink which forbid me from seeing our treasure. Her nails are on my prison tattoo. I am a poor man and bad drunk, reckless driver, couple counts of involuntary manslaughter...but a decent father.

Pleading with the hiccups, all reason is the weight within my arms. I can see their knees through the slants. Hear them breathing as they crouch beneath the ratty furniture, the sofa where the boxes of baby toys lie unopened. The packages are still wrapped in reindeers, Santa, and elves. Cobwebs and rat feces have collected upon the ribbons and bows and my cards in their colorful envelopes ignored by the bottles and extra nipples and dragon toys neglected.

Four chubby fingers on the paint, the shutters spreading and a litigator with soiled makeup smiles down at my daughter lying in the shadows of her great-grandfather's sweaters. Drips of perspiration trickle from stale armpits as they lift the gift of God, prying the imaginary degenerates from my shoulders.

I am cooking the cancer beneath the heater of their clown car as we pull away from the house. The baby is crying and we are driving so fast that their briefcases are bouncing in the backseat. Her hiccups more frequent and louder as the steering wheel blisters my palms and for one glorious embrace in the ether, eye-to-eye, diaper rash the least of our problems. Falling asleep has never been so easy.

The Evolution of Granny's Panties

Carlos Beto is sitting in our driveway in his Toyota Prius, picking boogers and flicking them through his sunroof. Behind the curtain in the master bedroom, we watch the meticulous process: his armpit hair blowing in the breeze as he raises his latest nasal offerings, tidbits floating featherlike against a sun-baked windshield. Cicadas release mating calls and the cherry angiomas on his scalp are glistening as they absorb the obstinate afternoon sunshine.

Sweating into his leather seat, there seems an endless cavern from which to dig. Twenty minutes vanish. An hour and the ambitions throb through fingernails grimed by yellow and black treasures. Thunder in the distance, but unperturbed, we huddle, naked, against the soft fabric—that my mother drank seven margaritas hanging to ascertain nothing was lopsided—cushioning our kneecaps, twirled around our thighs, crammed into our buttocks.

I wince with the fresh sunburn, the fluorescent Aloa vera spread upon white impressions beneath caresses of elfin thumbs, and the ectopic sebaceous glands rising, as my stepsister Ashley inches closer, gripping granny's magic wand. Carlos Beto flicks his soul. We lose our bodies in the curtain. Cold rain pelts the opaque window with horizontal ambushes and the driveway disappears along with all its grotesque mysteries—the cicadas silent—everything dead except the rising smell of garlic breath and raindrops and petrichor; soaked Rhododendrons merging into scattered soil.

I do not know how long the lightning-illuminated Manuela Beto was watching speechless with the laundry basket full of mother's underpants—but there she is in the corner gripping the plastic handles, grimacing into the storm, speechless, forlorn. There is nothing for us to do except open the bottom dresser drawer where mother keeps her granny panties and fill it to the brim. We lose electricity and nothing matters but the soft intricate texture of cotton panties as Manuela Beto whispers words to Ashley about *niños locos*.

Dios Mio!

In-between serene flashes of lightning followed by humongous crashes of thunder—which rattle and tilt picture frames of an unrecognizable and skinnier family from fancy vacations decades before my mother's madness—Manuela Beto races around the bedroom and stuffs the laundry basket with our abandoned clothes. She folds them and then sprints into the rain, toward the boogers, into the Prius.

Through the dying torrents we can decipher two

bloody taillights beckoning through the storm, and the drone of an engine fading into muddy puddles on the road. Soon, the fury passes and the cicadas come to life, and chasing the mucus toward a moonless evening, Carlos Beto swerves into traffic. His wife's nostrils are clogged with raindrops.

***

The next morning, Carlos Beto's Prius is sitting in our driveway. Through the sand in my eyes, I see them kissing and the passenger door is jolted with a rusty moan. Fluorescent butterflies hover around the hood and the sunroof is open. I rub the yellow rheum from my eye sockets and drop the crusted flakes out the window where they sprinkle the wet grass.

Manuela Beto is crop-dusting: farting in silence as she swaggers from kitchen to hallway with the vacuum cleaner hose wrapped around her neck like a

Boa restrictor. African sculptures glisten in the crisp morning sunlight. The house is ours again. We can smell the bacon and eggs sifting through the crop-dusting. Our appetites spoiled by the residual stench of an old woman who watches us out the cracked corner of her glass eye: shining bright and brown.

***

Last night Ashley crept into my bed beneath the Metallica posters and tucked her limbs between the eggshell mattress foam and my sunburn. Her silk pajamas so soft and cool against my strawberry skin, her tiptoes danced and floated on the floorboards. The moon spun itself in dyslexic spindles. The grandfather clock issued an angry tolling melody, desperate, as if hoping to warn the master bedroom from the cancerous grave. The rhythmic midnight bellow echoed and answered against the exorbitant Egyptian cotton her father spoils us with.

His whole house moaning with an intangible expurgation of money and decay—though mom is happy with her husband—no more running from Safeway and other grocery stores with Fruit Loops and Doritos and Polly-O String Cheese tucked inside her granny panties. No more Salvation Army underpants. No more Corona runs from Chevron. No more questioning the multivalent structure of the universe. No more moving furniture after Mom sprains her ankle during a brazen theft at Circle K.

***

Manuela Beto has never made love in this house—does not understand what it feels like to ride the lightning—to be carried up and outward through the vast open night clinging to an adolescent hope that tomorrow might bring something better. The cathartic egg carton: a magic carpet. Manuela Beto knows little about the carbon dioxide leaving our lungs, and how Ashley's nipples grow hard like hailstones, falling, not hurting.

There is a burning atavistic energy which flickers like

the return of electricity after a long drought, or a short

famine; and there we were in the magic of fireflies and

clutching straws, trying to build the ladder back to that

majestic dreamscape. Surreal and shattered, swallowed

by this knowledge of the planet and the folds of an

adolescent girl, taking something soulless which will

never be returned or replaced. The frantic search for

loins that have not prepared themselves for furious

battles beneath stormy skies which steal the moon for

moments, and then spit it out as if it were a tumor seed

lodged in a strawberry throat.

Carlos Beto told his wife to confess. They must

have been resting on their soiled twin mattress sweating

into the fluorescent streetlight which pours from the

avenue into their apartment, while we made love to

Master of Puppets blasting in my headphones. Through the sunburn, on the porch, I can smell Ashley.

Our mission: to hunt the crop-duster. Put an end to her poison. Manuela Beto must be silenced before she puts an end to our head-banging. We decide that drowning is the wisest option. It is cloudy, but Ashley floats on her inflatable zebra from corner to corner naked as I lure the unsuspecting Manuela Beto to the edge of the pool under the guise of curiosity. She is a five-foot, heavyset woman who never learned to swim, and hits the water like a bridge jumper reluctant to die. Using the pool skimmer, we take turns beating her cheekbones and knuckles to keep her away from the edge—shoving the unlucky Ecuadorian immigrant toward the center. Manuela Beto is screaming and cursing *Dios Mio* as her glass eye bounces on the surface. The cleaning snakes coil on the bottom of the pool. Manuela Beto spits cold chlorine at the thickening cumulonimbus,

coughing, bleeding from her skull.

We drag her unconscious body from the pool.

The glass eye watches us, scolding, brighter and browner

than ever before. We melt into the pavement and clean

the blood from the deck as if it were a sport fishing boat

after a glorious morning at sea. The water is pinkish in

plumes from Manuela Beto's wounds, but Ashley

disperses the blood with a series of impressive

cannonballs and backwards summersaults in pike

position. The zebra floats as if nothing even happened.

***

Banging your stepsister is so metal. Everybody

knows that. We wait for Carlos Beto to arrive, listening

for the decrepit engine of his Prius struggling up the

steep road through the trees. We drag his wife's body

through the sycamores and I dig a hole 'til the ground is

nothing more than rocks and puddles and our bodies are covered in poison ivy outbreaks. We can smell Manuela Beto through the dirt, on our skin. We bury the body and cover it with wet grass as if nothing occurred, like lightning after the storm. I pick the glass eye from the swimming pool with the skimmer basket and toss it into the road.

Carlos Beto pulls into our driveway, fingers lodged in his nostrils, searching for something that cannot be found, something that is gone for good— though he does not realize it yet. The sunroof is open and we watch his flicking, wondering what he is thinking, how he will cope with life without his wife. When the sun sets and the cicadas leave to make room for the bioluminescence of fireflies, Carlos Beto frees his fingers and rings the doorbell.

We answer. We shake hands. He smells different

38

than his wife and this is the first time we have seen him up-close. He walks out in the street to search, as if unable to accept our suggestion that his wife has not been seen since early morning. He returns with her glass eye in his palm as if holding a lightning bug. He unfurls his hairy fingers to show us the treasure, but we already know what's inside, and how to get it. There is nothing this man can show us that we do not already know.

Sunken Ancestry

We were in our cabin watching the rainbow through the porthole when you told me that Grandma jumped ship. The cruise liner was turning around and the sirens began to wail, and we could feel the weight of the Carnival Splendor shift if we focused on our bodies and not the spectrum of life spun from the thunderstorm. We wondered what inspired the brave woman to embrace the sea when nobody was looking.

Before that we were putting on our bathing suits, having just made love. It felt angry, but necessary. Mesmerized by the pillows in my face, the middle of your madness spilling over like a frozen margarita poured into a Mexican hand-blown glass by the pool deck.

Before that the retractable sky dome protected us.

Before that we were playing mini golf. Grandma was making love to her ice cream, lips glistening with euphoria. She was happy, thanked us for this treat: a vacation without depression, away from the monotony of a down economy and Alzheimer's.

Before that we were getting drunk, watching storm clouds thicken and drift faster in cooling wind. Grandma won at shuffleboard, I handed her five bucks, and granted permission for her afternoon snack.

Before that Grandma was taking a nap.

Before that we were eating lobster tails and drinking champagne. There was mariachi music and regional Mexican dancing. Beautiful folks were falling in love again as young maidens offered trays of white zinfandel and chardonnays. A crowd gathered in a circle and clapped.

Before that we were helping Grandma get dressed. Her head had developed a sore, and we brushed her wig back to get a closer look at what we were dealing with.

Before that we were riding on the water taxi back to the ship. It felt so good to be onshore, amid the palm trees munching seafood omelets.

Before that we told Grandma that we were more than friends; we were engaged. She seemed happy, sunk back in her deck chair, embracing the rhythm of brass instruments making love to her hearing aids. We had come clean. The anchor had been lifted.

Why You Should Be Nice to the Lady at the Laundromat

Because the lady at the Laundromat knows everything.
She plays connect the dots with the stains on your
clothes. She sees those things that you would never show
anybody else. She never judges, at least not out loud. She
pretends she doesn't notice, or she just pretends that it's
normal, nothing to be startled by. She smiles, clothes all
folded nicely and tight in a plastic bag. She knows what
you did last night, what you'll do tonight, and how the
clothes you're wearing right now will look next week.
Be nice to her because she's with you all the time, every
moment knowing what's happening. She can smell you
and all your debauchery. She might stick her head inside
the washer in the middle of the spin cycle and compare
that fragrance with the atavistic aromas of your clothes
in the bundle you brought in before she rinsed it out.

43

Now it's rainbows and waterfalls and perhaps she sticks her head inside the bag to smell a week of madness, sad that your clothes are now fresh, perfumed. She smiles when she sees you; loyal like a familiar neighborhood dog that recognizes your body odor before you turn the corner. A corpse smells better than your dirty laundry bag sometimes, but that dog likes the nastiest things, sleeps in things you would never imagine, places you've never been. But you've been elsewhere, strange places, stains complacent that not even warm water and three days of scrubbing in the sink will wash away.

The current cycle spins and spins while she smiles a benevolent clairvoyant grin, looks forward to another week or two, all the while looking back over her shoulder, the bouquet of the past dancing in her nostrils, the hairs in her nose interwoven with the aroma of your

empty dirty laundry bag, her head inside, one whiff away

from suffocation.

Once Got Busy in a Burger King Bathroom

I wipe a coagulated wad of cheddar from my bloody gums onto the plastic toilet paper dispenser as I release my bowels into a Burger King bathroom beside a stranger in the handicapped stall. It is always the same man, but different conversations are interrupted by diners, or elderly vagrants washing ankles and beards in the sink. The manager kicks them out.

"Only an ugly man can get arrested for cutting his toenails," the voice says.

We flush in unison, as if nodding. The plumbing has spoken its own language. An expurgation, grunt, or wipe means more than a wink of an eye.

"Can you smell stars falling; can we see the moon tonight?" I ask.

He slides his shiny shoe under my partition. The

hole in his black sock smiles, the frayed wool winks.

"Only a beautiful woman can get away with trimming her toenails," he says.

I study his hairy calves as he raises his khakis. I wonder what his wart wants, how it will taste. We flush in unison. He exits first. I avoid temptation to gaze through the hole. Tilt my head and screw my eyes.

"What will happen without hydrogen?" I ask.

I flush and wipe again, a stranger alone on his favorite throne. My tears splash warm water and bubbles bounce from ripple to mildew, echoing among the porcelain urinals and booger-stained walls. I place my face against the graffiti like a little boy stuffing his sunburned ear into a conch, listening to the ocean.

"When will the world end?" I ask.

The man moans. He flicks the lights as he slinks

47

away into the abyss of burning grease and clogged

arteries. I can smell the soda fountain machine rotting

through his skin. There is more to this man than his

bowel movements. He is made of stars and dust. There is

more to us all. Though we often bottle lightning in the

most obscure of places.

Muskie Doll Maker

Life is the shit in Pee Pee Township, Ohio. I nudged one nostril shut with my knuckle and snorted a fourteen-inch festoon of fire ants melting into a pineapple popsicle.

Soaked colonies somersaulting—catapulting into a labyrinthine vine of poison ivy with withered leaves and white peach-fuzzed berries spiraling up splintered wood—camouflaging the rickety barn. Barney bet me eighty bucks I wouldn't have the balls. I watched a wreath of fire ants glowing in my belly.

"¡Feliz Navidad!" Barney said.

Druggies at P.P. High called him Eight-ball Barney. So did the dudes at Pee Pee Lanes: fiends with alley cat eyeballs, turkey haulers with Keystone guts jiggling over the bubblegum-coagulated counter where Grandpa doled out fetid bowling shoes. Grandpa lived on whisky, funeral potatoes, Chiquita bananas, muskies, sawdust, and chunks of Vicodin. He swigged from a two-liter Sprite bottle marinated by a rattlesnake shedding its skin into tequila.

"Open the door," Barney said.

"It burns my face," I said.

"It's okay," Barney said.

Barney shattered a Noche Buena bottle across a caterpillar with cloudy vision and licked the stone, poison ivy and all.

"Yippee ki-yay," he said.

He spit into his armpit and cracked the cap with amber incisors. Curly black hairs hung from wet lips. Barney unzipped his cargo shorts and yanked out his foot-long penis.

"The pump is working," he said.

I turned away, grunting.

"Look at all these veins," he said.

Barney's voice changed when he exposed himself.

"Why did you do it?" I asked.

"I like dead bodies," he said.

Barney sniffled and you could hear the acoustics of frayed nostrils—cartilage chiseled from years of cocaine and meth and pills, the chill of broken bones, the rich temporary thrill of marrow donated weekly. Barney pumped iron at P. P. High.

"I got busy in a Burger King bathroom," Barney said.

Barney pissed toward the wreath of poison ivy. Urine didn't bother me much. The wind was blowing in the opposite direction.

"Mr. Wilson is humongous, huh?" Barney asked.

I counted the veins larger than #2 pencils, a maze

more ominous than the one carved into Old Man Temple's cornfield on the outskirts of Pee Pee Township.

"Two tweens lost in the labyrinth last night," Barney said.

"It's larger than yesterday," I said. "You'll be ready for the New Year's party."

"Better be," Barney said.

"Did they eat corn husks?" I asked.

"They ate DMT and shrooms."

"Damn," I said.

"They froze to death. Deputy Dave said they're still stuck together in the morgue."

"Let me go," I said.

Barney released me. Cumulonimbus sinking into dying moons, the ants glowing inside me—brighter— inching closer to my rectum.

"You're really gonna do it?" I asked.

He stuck his penis into a wreath of fire ants crowning a nucleus of poison ivy.

"Hell yeah, Sis," Barney said.

Barney boasted about breaking into the ancient graveyard when all the neighbors were at the party getting wasted to commemorate another year. It was the only night Deputy Dave's son wasn't guarding the graves. Some of the settlers robbed stagecoaches and Chippewa Indians. They were buried with rags, riches, headdresses, pockets weighted with silent promises.

"Corpses are my kryptonite," Barney said.

"Superman underpants are hard to find," I said.

***

Grandpa never missed his shift at Pee Pee Lanes—even when he was vomiting blood. Grandma texted to tell me he was missing. She hadn't seen him since he went to bed. Barney was great at rolling *primos*: Siamese joints of Alaskan Thunderfuck sprinkled with cocaine from Jalisco.

"When I woke he was gone," Grandma said. "The house reeked of stale dog farts.

Diego Maradona was licking his scrotum when I walked into the kitchen. His truck was here."

We searched the house. It was a diminutive dilapidated single-story home where some of the first settlers' surviving grandchildren congregated to get drunk in the 1840s. All the addicts lived. Most the teetotalers died during harsh winters and dank disease-cloaked summers. Hundreds of men pissed themselves in the winter of 1872. Some things never change.

***

Barney is my Siamese brother. We were born conjoined at the nose. We inhale what the other is doing miles away. I lost my virginity in Pee Pee Creek to a boy whose face looked like a prized Muskellunge: wide-mouthed, jagged-toothed, jaundiced, bloated—deprived of oxygen, atavistic, ferocious. Barney could smell me from our house.

"Come on," said Barney.

His face mauve, Barney yanked his zipper. He moved sluggishly, a dreary dinosaur, fossilized fragments of cirrhosis, footsteps fading into fire ants—rancid. We guzzled the last six Noche Buenas. Barney smashed some cancer pills and we snorted them on the rock. The poison ivy would keep away Uncle Rick at Christmas after turkey dinner. Rick was a seven-foot-tall amateur sumo wrestler and aspiring porn star. He was three years older than me and Barney but he lassoed us to his canopy bed four times already: Easter, Fourth of July, Thanksgiving, and Yom Kippur. Rick had eight arms, octopus eyeballs, three giant legs—a scabbed pimpled penis larger than Barney's—swooping back and forth to the moan of the wood frame, bandanas in split mouths, bleeding down his shaft.

"Let's go find Grandpa," Barney said.

***

We walked without words, woken by the sound of Pee Pee crackling in the static cold breeze, smoking exhaust pipes, aluminum and metals in our blood, rusty water in the fountains of Pee Pee Park and Edison Elementary.

"So horny," Barney said as we trudged past the ancient graveyard.

Kenny Dickens waved when he saw us. Kenny loomed, elfish, smoking a Camel Wide on a tombstone. Kenny was a weird kid who would never enter a courtroom. A juvenile delinquent, Kenny rose to local fame as a fraternity brother at Ohio State. He got

expelled his senior year for hazing. Two black dudes

died, but Kenny was never charged with any crime. Four

brothers are rotting in Allan-Oakwood Correctional

Institution.

  "I'm gonna dig the dirt faster than shit," Barney

said.

  "Call *The Guinness Book*," I said.

  Grandma was the bomb. She blasted Cam'ron

and puffed purple haze. She had fake boobs but a

beautiful face—no wrinkles. No hint of Grandpa

urinating on her forehead in the mildew bathtub. A

matriarch of Pee Pee Township, Grandma snorted the

medicine cabinet round-the-clock and this instilled

courage.

  "Hey, Grandma," Barney said.

  She kissed our cheeks.

"Kids!"

I woke embedded in Grandma's mattress.

"Grandpa wasn't in the barn," Barney said.

Truth was we never made it inside. Barney exposed his horse dong and then we sort of got drunk and forgot.

"Have you kids been huffing?" Grandma asked.

I shrugged as Barney nodded. There was no hiding anything from Grandma.

"Again?" Grandma asked.

"Yup," Barney said.

Grandma called an Uber.

"We need to check the barn," Grandma said.

"Why?" I asked.

"Detective Dave picked up a signal from his cell phone," Grandma said. "A Titleist."

"A ping?" I asked.

58

"Yeah, Detective Dave called before you came," Grandma said.

"Deputy Dave," I said.

Grandma nodded.

"He called," she said.

We hustled to the curb to smoke a Camel Wide. Grandma asked for a drag. The Uber driver honked. It was Uncle Max, a convivial drunk.

"Just tryin' to make an extra buck," Uncle Max said.

We shuffled into his Taurus. It was clean and legal and he got it when the cops bashed his head into the pavement one eerie night in Michigan by an insignificant Great Lake.

"Aren't we all," Grandma said. "To the barn— step on it!"

Uncle Max hit the accelerator and the engine

purred. Max was no pussy. Nobody can say the Peacocks are cowards. We're convicts; fishermen; corpse fuckers; penis pump purchasers; prostitutes; farmers; thieves; drug dealers; addicts; fiends; wrestlers; school shooters; Burger King drive-thru employees.

"Faster," Grandma said.

The roads wept empty. Everybody was home doing drugs or playing Bingo at Pee Pee Church of Christ. When we arrived, Deputy Dave was dead, bleeding into the wreath of poison ivy. Fire ants blanketed him—caked in mucus, blood, urine, castles of coagulated semen.

"He killed him," Grandma said.

We ushered her into the barn. The heavy door heaved. Horses neighed. We trudged through Augean squalor and climbed the frail wooden stairs to the cattycornered loft. We listened to Grandpa singing.

Uncle Sal and Kenny Dickens whimpered, hogtied to the trough filled with fire ants. Uncle Sal and Kenny ambled, petrified eyes fatter than flying saucers, duct-taped mouths mumbling drunkenly.

"Welcome," said Grandpa.

Grandpa's voice hoarse, he stood, butt-naked, sweating into a mule. The loft was blooming with settlers, dolls stuffed with sawdust. The walls ballooning, ceiling crumbling, rotting rafters trembling.

"Why is handsome Detective Dave dead?" Grandma asked.

"Deputy Dave," I said.

Grandma nodded.

"How ya haul the trough up these stairs?" Barney asked.

Grandpa didn't say anything. Flies swarmed, bathing in our eyeballs, nostrils, ears. The dolls started moving, crying, driven by fire ants and cicadas.

"These are amazing," Grandma said, admiring the eyes of a young girl.

"Just like the settlers," I said.

"Where did you find these old clothes?" asked Grandma.

"I embalmed them with salt and baking soda," Grandpa said.

He smiled wider than the world, brighter than a billion bulbs.

Barney undressed them and entered earths from centuries dead, peeling headdresses from flayed faces, making love with wild abandon as Grandpa hovered above. The barn moaning, we watched Barney and Grandpa taking turns. I listened to reindeers and sleigh bells, toboggans dancing in my mind—the barn shaking and moaning—the little boys and girls so alive—so free.

"Merry Christmas," Grandpa said.

Tribal reveries flowed through hardened arteries. Fire ants rolled into a colony of shrapnel—rising and falling, tiny eyeballs of toddlers calling me—forward, backwards—into the youthful bowels of a farmhouse filled with flames—elegant and tatterdemalion dolls wrapping rotting arms around me.

I see an ocean of eternity unfurling every morning, muckies churning in burning gut, Grandma getting down to business—cutting greedily with grimy fingernails through tattered clothes and ancient orifices—watching us out the corner of bloodshot sclarea. The matriarch of Pee Pee Township, wreathed in glory, grimacing with sawdust on rotting amber incisors.

A Smuggler's Atlas

We loaded the canisters with dope and fired them across the moonlit desert into Arizona. Soup cans stuffed with cocaine capable of landing a thousand feet from the border. The canisters were colored to classify who launched them. We catapulted them into fields. If the Border Patrol discovered them floating on the Colorado River, someone was liable to lose an earlobe. The pneumatic cannon can misfire, errors were unavoidable.

We knew every constellation. We fired hundreds of kilos of cocaine into rotting saguaros. This was our sport—careers were bought and sold. Carbon dioxide tanks on our shoulders, blood vessels hardened by arteriosclerosis. It was better than chopping heads, or being ambushed by a sport utility vehicle pumping automatic weapons, or throwing a Molotov cocktail into an Acapulco nightclub.

Brush up to our shoulders; we were close enough to launch loogies at the border fence. Our fingers blistered, knuckles purple, puss poured from calluses. We did this every night with the gringo farmer. We aimed for his fields.

When the work was done and our muscles were aching, we drove home, waving to the Policía with our giant rusty cannon reflecting the rising sun, a decadent middle finger to the Border Patrol. The whole village watched us; most residents too poor for vehicles. Our neighbors despised us and grinned through clenched incisors.

Sixty percent of the cocaine that passes into Arizona goes through our town, our tunnel. Smugglers stay overnight while waiting for clandestine vehicles to load with invisible marching powder for other parts of the border.

During the seasonal debauch, samples of
unlimited products are provided for all to enjoy. The
people get so wired when the smugglers leave town that
they start building elaborate makeshift houses made out
of plywood and tarps, but then the drugs wear off and the
houses are in worse shape than before.

***

It is the unkempt roadside crosses that attract me
most: those beneath murderous curves, twisted
guardrails, mangled vehicles moaning in the wind. They
drive with broken headlights, charred vehicles rusting for
decades, or disintegrated. The fatalities are seldom
innocent; drivers are often struck by fortunate cows. The
corpses who wear seatbelts are melted until the
Bomberos carry plastic plates with barbecue onto the
truck, reeking of mesquite and alcohol.

There are hundreds of kilometers with no

Bomberos, no hospitals—no hope. Call a tow truck from a tiny village and drag up the body. Many plummets go unreported. The invisible islands of the night—where spirits whisper melodies as sirens careening from the *carreterra* with a vehicle full of beer cans.

My headlights reflect the roadside *Cuervo Peligroso* warnings: Dangerous Curves. I always pray after midnight, when only the most insane of ageless truck drivers are plowing through the mountains—tires nudging the ledge, decapitating rabbits, tossing gravel toward corpses, roaring rigs covered with graffiti coiling around the narrow starlit abysses with the wisdom of chariot-donning warriors returning from the afterworld.

The *carreterra* is tight near shrines. I must park kilometers away then hike upward or downward toward the scene of the beautiful death: plummeting through the scenery of a postcard, that final moment floating into the ethereal landscape of dazzle—mesmerized by wind

rippling through exploding eardrums with beer cans

rattling against the roof of a cavern. Careening from the

carreterra into shards of twisted steel, moaning to a

cathedral speckled upon the pebbles and boulders for

vultures to worship.

I park next to the abandoned farm where bandits

siphon gasoline from a rusty barrel to tourists unaware of

the distance between *gasolineras*. The bastards do not

bother me or my Toyota. Bandits respect these

memorials. I wipe my sweat with a towel before

kneeling next to the altar. I clean the debris from the

wooden crosses and the spider webs from the abandoned

candles. I light their wicks, place fresh flowers, and clear

the dead foliage andgarbage thrown from vehicles. I

walk down that cavern toward the cars and pick the

neglected possessions from the remnants. There is

always something new.

When the vehicles are in decent shape, I crawl inside and listen to the echoes of the dying, my knuckles massaging the rust and coarse defecations adorning charred chariots; but at this particular curve, nothing is able to withstand the jagged boulders which mark the entry to the butterfly-strewn desert.

***

The tunnel connecting San Ysidro to Tijuana traverses three miles and costs more money than any drug tunnel ever built. It never ends. We supervise teenagers loading robotic wagons. The bottom is magnetic and it glides like an airport passenger between gates. The electronic floor is so shiny that it glimmers through the thickest of human eyelids. The passage is illuminated with bulbs that never die, and nobody knows how long the tunnel has existed. None of the employees remember its construction. The sophistication is well beyond the mediocre structures of the Border Patrol checkpoints and their flimsy fence, which the tunnel passes through at no less than six different intervals.

My uncle lives in one of those houses on the other side and sometimes we dig into the bedrooms of relatives. The cartels need every passage they can get. We have no idea how many exist. We follow our routes. We digest dinner as green and white Border Patrol vehicles cruise the street out front. We wave when they watch us through the windows, with warm tortillas in our mouths.

We have many wounds. My wrists and forearms are scarred form the casino fire. We could hear the slot machines and the muffled chorus of screaming patrons asphyxiating in bathrooms waiting for their faces to melt. We shouted for them to leave before igniting the gasoline, but some proceeded to the back, presuming there was an unlocked exit—there was not. We filled the front with flames. I dragged two waitresses to safety. I saw my face in the flames, and later in the bricks of cocaine, sculpted with such glory and precision.

***

Your first gunfight makes you a man, whether you die in a pool of blood beside the passenger door of a Pathfinder, or survive to spit bullets from automatic weapons another day. My grandfather was involved in my first gunfight.

Balacera is what we Mexicans refer to as a gunfight. Gringos sometimes think of gunfights as western style shootouts with cowboys fingering leathering holsters. It is nothing of the sort. It is combat without military gear. Cars and houses and bodies are riddled with bullets. Three minutes go by like the flash of a firefly landing on your Adam's apple.

Grandpa was hit in the throat during the seventh minute. He prayed that the teenagers would be able to slay him painlessly. A stub of the toe and Grandpa would wince and sulk in his bedroom for hours. Grandpa was not killed fast. He slumped over the hood of the Pathfinder, clutching the gaping wound, mumbling amid the gunfire.

My brother charged the vehicle we ambushed, assassinated the driver to the drone of barking dogs. Humans never speak after a good gunfight. I carried Grandpa on my shoulders until he grew heavy. The grass swallowed him as ambulances and police vehicles engulfed us.

My brother hanged himself in his holding cell with his cowboy belt. The buckle was embedded into his throat in the same spot where Grandpa was shot. I punched the walls till my knuckles bled and disappeared. A year later, rolled out of prison in a laundry truck filled with feces and urine.

***

I was ambushed in the rental car when my son was sleeping in the backseat. The boy was blasted through his skull. But it did not kill him—only made him speak sentences backwards and pump bullets with venom. This instance turned the boy into a savage and word has it he decapitated fifty foot soldiers of Las Zetas before being flayed alive. That is no easy task, let me tell you. This is a family affair.

***

The procession of vehicles waiting to make it through the border patrol checkpoint into San Diego meanders its way through children soiled with filth who peddle trinkets with yellow teeth. Their parents wave water bottles and refreshments in the air above anemic skulls. The women get so close to the car that you can see their armpit hair. The abnormally long one leads the way. It curls itself around the window and threatens to enter. This black coarse reminder of what life would be without the cartels tucks itself on the tinted edge of the window, my thumb on the button to make it disappear. They are nothing without us: these children. No different than the kids and adults on the other side of the border. We are modern-day saviors who risk our lives every second to deliver the shipments that provide the medicine that Americans need. Without people like me, the prices would skyrocket. The cars coil into rattlesnakes and you can hear the instruments and the children sitting on the dashboard of the affluent, wiping windshield with spit. I nod, safe behind sunglasses.

They tug on my wipers, swipe the glass with

hairless elbows. The children would give anything to be on that other side of the border. I shove one of them into the trunk. Two others force themselves inside and we race toward the Gringos with their machine guns aimed at my face. I hit the brakes and skid marks fill my shorts. They drag me from the vehicle. You can hear the children banging on the trunk, begging for America.

The kids are freed and escorted back across the border—but they run—fast as their sandals will allow—these illegal immigrants sprinting toward paradise, chased by Border Patrol agents to the sound of honking horns in honor. Delighted, some Mexicans shout *Órale* from their windows. Sweaty men with no air condition in their trucks pump their fists. Knuckles are the exuberance of a new nation, one where detainment never matters. The cars celebrate these young pedestrians with no chance of escaping.

The residual odor in my trunk attracts dogs and the agents lead me into their decrepit office—nothing compared to the house of a smuggler.

"You speak English?" they ask.

The men have Mexican accents as thick as my parents'. Their skin is darker than mine, and their arms are the same length as my dead sister's. There is not much difference in our heritage. Our genitals are the same. Except my balls are bigger, larger than you have ever seen, and the measurements are something that prison guards can confirm should anybody desire to track them down.

"English is my language," I tell them.

They nod and lick their lips.

"Hope those goddamn wetbacks get some food and water before they return to the squalor," I say.

"What is your citizenship?" the agent asks.

I tell them the truth. There is nothing left to die for. Smuggling is a business and the bastards will breathe into your eyelashes with wicked odor. I tell myself (in English) to remain calm: *You are detained by gringos. Their wall is nothing. People are crawling through it as we speak.*

***

My instructions were to strangle my attorney. Guys like me always get the best lawyers. He sat across from me in the holding cell, my legs shackled to the table to prevent a repeat of my tantrum that caused the concussion of two other inmates and the broken nose of an inhospitable guard.

My attorney told me that Las Zetas targeted his daughter for getting men like me acquitted. He drove around in a bulletproof Hummer to the tunes of Mozart, smoking cigars down to his fingers and then digging them into the ashes of the cup holder. He said they tortured her naked and hung her from a bridge in Acapulco during spring break.

His daughter was merely doing beer bongs and flashing her mosquito bites. He told me that when he went down to identify the body—protected by thugs and goons paid twice his salary—her nipples were branded with warnings and her stomach was carved with a *Z*. Her fingertips were amputated and they decapitated her and put the video on YouTube.

It didn't matter; I had to kill him. My bosses had hired me for similar jobs with local Policía. This was my mission. The fireflies in his eyes and the wrinkles of his forehead warned me to abandon the idea. The poor soul was the same as me. I warned my attorney about the hit. I told the government everything they asked to avoid trial.

***

I wanted them to send me to some exotic country. Somewhere warm with monkeys jumping from banana trees and parrots to keep me company. They refused. I told them someplace with tacos and saguaros and mariachi, but ended up in Wisconsin with a common gringo name and a damn white picket fence covered in snowflakes. This was the first time I lived in a cold climate and it fit me—this old house by myself. I sat by the chimney, drinking tequila, burning pieces of the basement that I chopped with my axe. I waited for the cartel to bust down the door, and got fat from all the deer meat in my freezer.

Bambi was delivered by my amicable neighbor. He got me out of the house with the allure of smoking crystal and slaughtering animals during hunting trips. We killed bears and moose. It was no different than shooting thugs and gangbangers. It felt nice to bring down a beast bigger than El Chapo. But I was addicted to the pipe. The Program knew this and flew me out to a clinic for six weeks under the guise of visiting a dying aunt. The day after my return the neighbor was dead. Not from meth, but from a baby bear which tore into his bedroom in the middle of the night. He had a heart attack when the things started snuggling beneath the sheets.

The bear was hunted. The man was wheeled from his house. The animal was slaughtered and fallen from its branches, its face so tortured and surprised that it exuded the expression of a hirsute obese hunter. The authorities dragged the bear to a caged truck and tossed its corpse inside. The snow had some puddles of bear blood; and when I was alone I smothered myself in the viscous *sangre* and filled my house with smoke. I opened the door so the bear's mother would come inside.

***

After recovering from the mauling, the agents stuck me in the same house.

"You are one of America's Most Wanted," said the bear.

The animal would sit on the steps out front with the door barricaded with planks. There was nothing left of the basement; that is where I began sleeping after the deer returned and began creeping down the snow to peek into my windows while I dreamt. They darting away into the brush—these beatific creatures which once satisfied me so much. They started watching me in the kitchen. The snow covered the bottom half of the windows, but then it melted and the glass was covered in animal hides which attracted maggots and ants, but this did not bother me.

"What have you come for?" the bear asked.

Each day the bear grew wiser and larger and no longer was I afraid of her. I killed the deer that dashed through the glass window that cast no reflection. The ones who were not fatally injured were stitched up and given their rightful place at the dinner table. The bear did not return for months. Then the basement was shaking and the bear wrestled itself down the staircase. I was sure the animal had come to snuggle.

I was wrong. It took my eyes and strung them from the corners of the sockets for a second before slicing them with its claws. The deer did not offer assistance. The animal was serene after it disappeared, and sensing my ineptitude began to moan and cuddle on the filthy mattress filled with blood.

"This is your last chance to make a change," the bear said.

The animal was capable of keeping me warm. It

dragged me up the broken stairs and placed me on the shredded leather couch soiled by deer defecations. The beast seemed to push the hard briskets of feces and mud aside and shoved me into a pocket. The bear pulled me toward the fire, the legless couch dragging itself in victory against the bloodstained floorboards.

She positioned me near enough to keep warm without being close enough to burn. The hot putrid air of breath as it passed in exasperation through those moist motherly nostrils was a comfort I hadn't experienced since winning my first *balacera*. The snout with its whiskers tickling my neck made the pain diminish, but agony was what I had been missing in my life. It felt nice to be blind with the bear gnawing on food from the refrigerator.

She poured me a glass of whiskey and made sure I knew where the bottle was kept, and its distance was measured by my fingers no less than seven occasions to assure me that the Jameson was located in an ideal spot. She was loquacious and spoke elegantly about many topics that had never occurred to me.

The mahogany of the mantle was placed over my shoulders and stomped into dozens of pieces of wood for the fire. These were laid on my lap and beside my feet as the bear retreated into the woods.

***

I waited for the bear to return, but she never did. I spent all my time thinking about the things she said. I would tell her how things could be clearer with no eyeballs than the ice melting into my warm glass of whiskey. I had managed to crawl to the liquor cabinet and kept alive on the rotting carcasses of deer meat covered with maggots. Flies swarmed my eye sockets, so I covered them with a blanket and waited for the bear to show.

***

The agents shook me and their voices came through the stupor like lightning in the fog. They placed me in a hospital, and pumped me full of drugs and nutrients. The sweet nurse bathed me and shaved my face when I wanted to feel like a man again—not just some animal.

There wasn't much for me to hope for and The United States Federal Witness Protection Program could only carry me so far. They were convinced that I was insane, suicidal, and a threat to the men and women who kept visiting me at the hospital, offering their condolences and bloating me with chocolate. I fingered the balloons full of helium. They had to keep me protected, safe from those who wanted to castrate me and hang my headless corpse from an American bridge glimmering with steel.

There was still beauty in the world. More so than ever; the good of the planet crossing spheres could be sensed with tunnel vision and the dying souls entered my room through the vents at the top of the wall where the warm air kept us alive. I was able to take the pulse of the hospital with my nostrils, and one night when there was a thunderstorm so loud that human voices melted into nothingness, at last, I entered the elevator shaft with gusto and walked out the front door of the hospital.

***

Good thing about being blind was that the cartels would never expect it. So they shipped me out west, gave me another gringo name even more common, but this time they rented me a cheap one-bedroom apartment on Silverbell Road. It was decent. The small space was easy to manage, and I was able to dance around the furniture. Without sight, it is not necessary to have so much space. People do not realize this until they die, when the walls close in.

I took up golf and became popular at the driving range. I would hit the course with the men as their guest. They let me drive the cart across the fairways, and I floored the plastic peddle into the rubber beneath my cleats. One day I kept going, my Titleist gloves gripping the wheel with white knuckles—we catapulted the cart into the center of a sand trap. The guys laughed it off and let me to drive my own cart after that. I had memorized the course to a tee and indeed the University of Arizona campus could be maneuvered with ease. Within months, I had become a respected civilian, admired by affluent gringos. They would sit in my ratty apartment and mingle.

Another activity I enjoyed was hanging around

the nudist colony where one of my foursome worked as accountant. I was able to massage suntan lotion on the backs of the ladies who kept me company by the pool. The odor of jasmine borne by the desert, the giggles of the cougars, and groans of the old men who offered my cocktails, was the perfect accompaniment to the chirping of robins and the drone of bumblebees.

I was the envy of the country club and all men looked up to me, especially in the men's room, where I spent a great deal of time handing out fancy towels. I mesmerized them with my blue comb swimming in a jar of Barbicide. Dipping my wand into the cauldron, they would offer generous tips and enjoyed their minutes away from their wives or golf buddies. They shared their innermost secrets, and I knew who they were by the splash of piss against the urinal cake or the sound of gas emitted between expulsions in sparkling porcelain tanks secluded by smooth mahogany.

There was no monotony to their movements, and my life was perfect. For the first time, there were no worries about dying, or seeing into the future. The bear had given me the gift of illumination and the Witness Protection Program had turned me into a superhero. Every morning, a different woman from the country club would drive her husband's foreign car into Silverwood Terrace Apartments to fuck me on my grimy futon. Punks would smash their car windows with rocks and steal the pocketbooks and stereos. I told these ladies to take taxis, warned them of the vandals, but they ladies refused to listen, until they heard the echo of shattering glass during doggy style.

***

Silverbell Terrace was not a ghetto. It was indeed a decent place for college students and the working poor,

89

conveniently situated three miles northwest of the University of Arizona, just about where the city merges into desert and dirt roads. Silverbell Terrace had the maintenance man and gardeners. It had the cocaine cowboys and alcoholics. The grass was green. The pool was kept in pristine condition and the palm fronds were prevented from resting downward dead and depressed like many residents.

Many renters were ambitious. Some were heavy sleepers. The police helicopters were pervasive. The spotlights penetrated through the tapestries and curtains and duct tape and aluminum foil. The inertia of the rotors was so powerful that the dead flowers from my stolen trees bounced back and forth across the terrace in front of the door to my apartment.

You could hear a hundred toilets flushing at the same time; frantic fiends flushing their deviance down the shitter. I stole the trees from ABCO Desert Market after grocery shopping. Nobody ever suspects a blind man. Truth is that the police helicopter only arrived for armed robberies, usually at the ABCO. They do not come for stolen plants.

After morning sex, I pretended to read the latest issue of *Penthouse* in a chaise longue next to the swimming pool. I am ashamed of my nipples and my body. I never removed my t-shirt in public, and therefore had a perpetual farmer's tan and the manager whispered as she passed through the gates from her office to the paths that lead through meandering cacti and palm trees to the turquoise and tan apartments. I never wore sunscreen. My skin meant nothing to me. I collected hyper-pigmented dots and brown freckles to prove the illusion that I was human.

The Mexican maintenance man never formally

introduced himself—but he smiled and tossed marijuana grenades at my feet whenever he saw me walking. I clutched the plastic bags and pocketed them. He was a generous saint. I imagine he must have discovered ounces while cleaning out apartments. The tenants would snort the couches if possible. I found a fat rock of cocaine wrapped in a wad of *The Tucson Daily Star* in my rented couch the first week I moved in. Hours were wasting blowing this stellar rock and moving furniture, hanging speaker wires, and tweaking alone till a few hours before dawn. There must have been nearly a hundred dollars of Indian reservation marching powder.

Al was a Mexican ex-convict who lived on the second floor of the corner apartment closest to the south side of the parking lot, right above Jon Enriquez and his mother, the latter of whom had a tendency to peek out the windows at the pedestrians and pontificate all the rumors and truths despite her inability to speak a word of English.

We all had four units to our building and Silverwood Terrace was full of degenerates and vile individuals. This is not to say that there were not some decent people in the complex, but our four or five clustered buildings consisted of despicable hearts in at least a couple apartments and all of us had issues, even the girls who lived with kittens and the old men with tinfoil on their windows.

Cocaine was in most of those apartments. Weed was smoked by almost all of us and it was a neighborly miracle a few months after I moved in when I noticed four generations of degenerates, many of whom had never spoken to each other, establishing a crescendo of interactions and drug deals centered around the grass and asphalt and palm trees.

When I say that there were good people of lower income in the apartments--amid the criminals, dealers, users, students--there were Mexicans and poor families that were forced to live among us, and their children would ride rusty bikes and fly kites made from materials in Mom's kitchen with grimy fingers. The parents might have been great people, but their children taunted me. One especially loquacious seven-year-old would say: "You think you're sooooo cool...you think you're so cool."

I was six times his age, twice his height, and he chopped me down to the size of fire ants scurrying across Slushies. Everybody encouraged the incessant chants and smirk of this future cartel member. My adulterers were powerless to the pure visceral comedy of this little punk putting me in my place. I had to take it. Nodding my head like a dysfunctional narcoleptic turkey, bobbing to the rhythms of sadistic laughter from an eight-year-old bully.

***

The dichotomy between the country club people and my fellow residents of Silverbell Terrace could not have been clearer. Their voices, odors, vocabulary, styles of debauchery; I was a blind man trapped between two opposite worlds. And then, the boy was duct-taped to my bed, sweating into the pillowcase.

I carved flesh from his kneecaps and elbows and the tip of his nose, to the melody of birds beating their beaks against the window. I flayed him as I had done with members of the Gulf Cartel so many times. This boy who had made a mockery of me was remorseful.

No longer protected by the Gringos, I fled to Mexico, aware that there was no turning back, no way to avoid being tracked. It was only a matter of time. Still, I kept a low profile and rented a hut on the beach in Oaxaca. I had money saved, but knew that I would not need it.

Paranoia spun sandy moonlight from howling animals. I was unable to sleep. I spent most my waking energy collecting driftwood. The monkeys were plotting and soon they would attack. The skirmishes were a daily occurrence. They would pounce with the numbers to slaughter me in the depths of slumber. I was building a raft to sail into the Pacific.

***

My vessel was built by the fingers of a blind man and I had no way of ascertaining the craftsmanship. I half-expected the thing to sink soon after getting past the breakers that kept knocking me into the foam. My ankle was attached to the raft by knotted monkey tails. After an hour, things grew calm and I covered myself in the

Mexican blanket to protect my skin from the sun. I survived on tropical fish captured by lucky thrusts of a sharpened driftwood spear. I was able to warm the catch in the sun for an hour, wrestling pelicans the first few days, until they disappeared.

I starved for days and started eating the monkey tails until there was nothing left to connect me to the raft. One morning, the horn of the Carnival Elation knocked me into the waves borne by the ship. The reverberation was so loud that I could hear it beneath the surface, and grew convinced the ship was going to swallow me. I lost my raft. I could sense the shadow looming over me, shading me from the sun. My flesh was cold with the breeze. Men with Australian accents pulled me aboard a shuttle boat which journeyed toward an enormous debauch. I was welcomed with margaritas, music, and applause on the sundeck of the Carnival Elation. The

97

people reeked of suntan lotion, alcohol, and the aroma of gourmet food was clinging to the fluffy towels they wrapped me with. The salt on the rim tasted like the ocean and there was nothing between me and these Caucasian cruisers with their obsession for shuffleboard, buffet decadence, and driving golf balls off the upper deck.

One night after midnight brunch, upon overhearing about the moonlit beauty of the Baja, I excused myself to the bathroom and jumped off the eighth deck of the Carnival Elation. Cracked my skull against the ship but kept my cool as the water engulfed me and swam as the blood poured from my wound. The waves pushed me toward the shore, muscles driven by the inertia of a suicide jumper's mind in midair. It was difficult to measure the distance between me and the bottom of the cruise ship. This was not an Acapulco cliff dive. This was the first time my blind prescience had gone awry.

The waves knocked me against the corral and I knew it was the end. But something in the back of my head poured into my nostrils and I climbed the corral. The crabs scattered as I crawled. Sea urchins stabbed my kneecaps and elbows. Rolling into puddles, crabs pinched my hands and face. The tides would wash over me and bring more puddles, but I could measure the distance to the edges of this promontory by the sound of the waves on every side. I kept going till I could feel sand in the bottom of the puddles. When I arrived at the beach, I tossed my bloodied body into the waves and let the sea roll me back and forth.

When I woke to the rising tide the air was cool and the sounds of birds engulfed the canopies of trees. My skin was raw and through my eyelids I caught visions of the dead skinless boy. I could see his face

perfect before the savage act. From the job I did with the

flaying, I was able to trace the scars and wrinkles and

dimples and moles which littered his flesh. In my eyelids

he approached and asked for forgiveness. I could not

grant him that.

Monkeys came down from the trees. My dream

from the start: to get rich and live off the work of the

monkeys, their nimble fingers delivering dinners prone

to cause diarrhea. It was a perfect system. We would

lounge in hammocks and get lost in the horizon. These

monkeys did not see things as I did. They began slapping

my wounds and rubbing my skull. They ripped the

clothing from my skin.

The monkeys threw feces at me, hobbled away,

and here they left my bloodied body naked except for the

golf ball that had been lodged in the back pocket of the

trousers I had borrowed from one of the omelet chefs who befriended me at sea. I rubbed the craters on the Titleist as the moon rose higher and swallowed the sand in an attempt to choke, but the monkeys returned and cleaned out my windpipes. They kept me warm as I wept, and together our voices merged into the ocean.

***

The rain soaked the island every afternoon. The palm trees were very tall and I was only able to climb a couple because they had many twists and turns where hurricanes had blown them horizontal. Each morning I walked the perimeter: a short distance of perfect sand interrupted by the corral outcropping. I plucked sand dollars with my toes and laid starfish for my bed and pillow. Each day I would collect a new batch. I sharpened driftwood on stones until the wood was burning and stabbed my kneecaps, elbows, and earlobes—peeling the flesh and then ripping the cartilage from my nose with my fingernails.

The coconuts were so sparse that the monkeys fought for them and attempted to steal the chunks of smashed fruit. They would disappear to their trees and I would chuck rocks at the tops, hoping to hit a wayward coconut. When one landed, the monkeys would take it, but I would wrestle with great hunger over the coconut before they were able to escape with it. They bit pieces of my flesh and these gangrene chunks were flayed off beneath the rain. But then the coconuts ran out. The monkeys stayed in their trees, and once in a while they would fight for food and one would drop to its death against the corral.

They left me to die. I would sit out in the sun, flaying pieces of my face, ripping out chunks of hair. I wanted to drown. The monkeys would return to earth to eat their murdered counterparts, and I would wrestle them for scraps, and my arms and legs and everywhere bore the mark of their teeth. I chopped their tails and ate them raw as the monkeys squirmed in anguish. Soon there were no more monkeys. I scattered the island searching for their carcasses before the savage birds would come down or the waves would carry the fallen monkeys to their watery graves.

The birds started dropping from the sky. I ate them raw and survived on the nutrients of dead fish washed ashore. Then the rains stopped. Everything stopped and there was no life on the island outside of my own skinless body. I started peeling the skin from my left foot, then the ankle, and kneecap, and hip. Soon there was no skin from the soles of my feet to the rim of my penis. My waist went next, followed by my torso, shoulders, back, and delicious buttocks. My arms and hands were fantastic, but then things got difficult. The neck was much more complicated, and it got to the point, where there was nothing left of my body. That is when I cut off my tongue. Insects were oppressive. They rose from my skin when I slept. I kept myself in the ocean all day. When the sailboat arrived, I was doing the dead man's float when the wife called out.

"Another cartel killing," said a man's voice.

I could hear the wife vomiting into the ocean.

"Turn away, Gary, please," she said.

The man growled and I rolled over, again and again until the woman was screaming and the man was cursing at me to grab the rope. I screamed that I was blind, but he did not understand what I was saying and then when he sailed closer he saw that my tongue was missing.

"Jesus Christ, mate!"

"What the hell happened to you?"

"Who did this?"

I told them everything, but the words were atavistic, not human. The man pulled me aboard and the wife cried. I could hear them talking about what to do with me. I had not moved in hours. They pontificated about infectious diseases.

"What the hell are these animals?" the wife asked.

The man groaned. He placed his ear against where my lips used to be and bubbles erupted from my mouth to assure him I was still alive. He tossed me into the water.

***

I began to grow new skin. Not everywhere, and not of the same texture as before, but the salt water and air seemed to help. The couple dropped me in the breakwater of the island where they found me floating, and the waves welcomed me to shore. There was no escaping my own skin, and it grew crusty and soon I was attached to the corral. I lay there in the sun and waited for the rains which never came, and the days floated into one. The engine of the cartel boat was an aberration, I was certain.

Acknowledgements

Stories originally appeared in these publications:

Zamboni   *Spilled Milk Magazine*

The Mexican Conductor   *concīs*

Canopy Bed   *Literary Orphans*

Crabs Feasting on Eyeballs   *Counterexample Poetics*

It's Not Delivery, It's DiGiorno   *b(O)INK*

Purple Heart   *The Airgonaut*

Crawlspace   *FRiGG*

Restraining Order   *Contrary Magazine*

The Evolution of Granny's Panties   *The Adroit Journal*

Sunken Ancestry   *decomP*

Why You Should Be Nice to the Lady at the Laundromat   *A-Minor*

Once Got Busy In a Burger King Bathroom   *Maudlin House*

Muskie Doll Maker   *Bridge Eight Press*

A Smuggler's Atlas   *Sententia: The Journal*

Cover art by Matthew Revert

I must honor the dead and the living. Thank you Ethan Matthew Dexter Torres, Frank Fitton, Rob Barton, John Enriquez, Geraldine Fasolo, Craig Wilson, Andrew Reynolds, Gifford T. Foley, Christina Goodman, F. Scott Fitzgerald, Zelda Sayre Fitzgerald, John Cheever, Ewen DeWitt, Raymond Carver, J.D. Salinger, Don DeLillo, Hunter S. Thompson, Edgar Allan Poe, Virginia Eliza Clemm Poe, and you!

Made in the USA
Las Vegas, NV
17 January 2024

84257981R00067